Celebrate reading with us!

Bookworm

Senior Author
John J. Pikulski

Senior Coordinating Author
J. David Cooper

Senior Consulting Author
William K. Durr

Coordinating Authors
Kathryn H. Au
M. Jean Greenlaw
Marjorie Y. Lipson
Susan E. Page
Sheila W. Valencia
Karen K. Wixson

Authors
Rosalinda B. Barrera
Edwina Bradley
Ruth P. Bunyan
Jacqueline L. Chaparro
Jacqueline C. Comas
Alan N. Crawford
Robert L. Hillerich
Timothy G. Johnson
Jana M. Mason
Pamela A. Mason
William E. Nagy
Joseph S. Renzulli
Alfredo Schifini

Senior Advisor
Richard C. Anderson

Advisors
Christopher J. Baker
Charles Peters
MaryEllen Vogt

HOUGHTON MIFFLIN COMPANY   BOSTON
Atlanta   Dallas   Geneva, Illinois   Palo Alto   Princeton   Toronto

10

People Who Write

14

🏵 Jimmy Lee Did It
by Pat Cummings

30

🏵 My Five Senses
by Aliki

52

🏵 The Surprise
by George Shannon

76

Writing with Pictures
an informational article

🏵 Award Winner

POETRY

48

Mari's Tooth
by Alberto Barrera
translated from Spanish

THEME BOOKS

The Great Sea Monster
by Berthe Amoss
Dance Away
by George Shannon

THEME 2

80

Old Favorites

84

⭐ Stone Soup
retold by Ann McGovern

106

⭐ The Three Little Pigs
retold by Paul Galdone

128

Baby Rattlesnake
told by Te Ata to Lynn Moroney

POETRY
127
The Old Woman Who Lived in a Shoe
a traditional rhyme
✿ The Old Woman
by Beatrix Potter

148
Favorite Rhymes Around the World
traditional rhymes

THEME BOOKS
✿ Whale in the Sky
by Anne Siberell
✿ The Princess and the Pea
a Hans Christian Andersen tale
illustrated by Eve Tharlet

156

PROBLEMS, PROBLEMS!

160

🏵 The Birthday Cake *by Ivar Da Coll*
translated from Spanish

190

Carry Go Bring Come *by Vyanne Samuels*

212

Hiccups and Sneezes
an informational article

216

🏵 Anna's Secret Friend
by Yoriko Tsutsui

8

POETRY

187

Whistling
by Jack Prelutsky

188

A Problem   *by Marchette Chute*

189

Shoe Laces   *by Leland Jacobs*

THEME BOOKS

My Dog and the Knock Knock Mystery
by David A. Adler

Jamaica Tag-Along
by Juanita Havill

READING SCIENCE

236

What's for Lunch?

GLOSSARY

242

People Who Write

The world is filled
with wonderful books and
with "bookworms" who
love to read them.   But
who are the people who
write the books?
All kinds of people —
that's who!
As you read these
stories and poems, you'll
find out about the people
who wrote the words and
made the pictures.

11

CONT

My name is Pat Cummings. I hope you'll enjoy my story, *Jimmy Lee Did It*. It begins on page 14.

My name is Aliki. I wrote and illustrated the book called *My Five Senses*, which begins on page 30.

Hello! I'm Alberto Barrera. I like to write poetry. In this book, you'll find one of my poems about my daughter Mari. It begins on page 48.

ENTS

Hi! I'm George Shannon. My story, *The Surprise,* begins on page 52.

We are Jose Aruego and Ariane Dewey. We worked together to make the pictures for *The Surprise*.

13

JIMMY LEE DID IT

by Pat Cummings

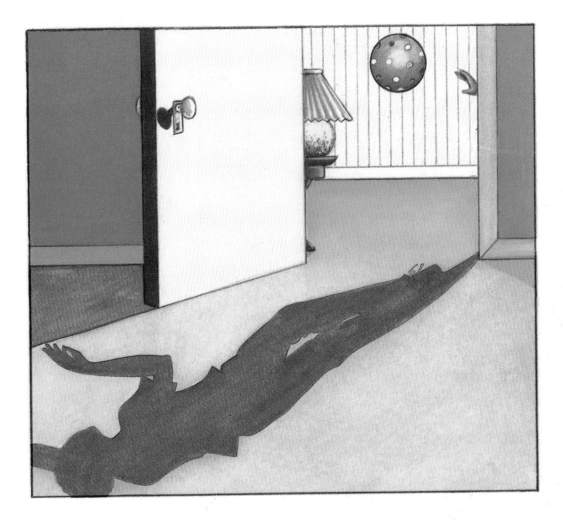

Jimmy Lee is back again
And nothing is the same.
He's causing lots of trouble,
While my brother takes the blame.

Artie made his bed, he said.
But Jimmy thinks he's smart.
While Artie read his comics,
Jimmy pulled the sheets apart.

Dad fixed us pancakes
And Artie said his tasted fine,
But Jimmy Lee had just been there
And eaten most of mine.

I heard the crash of breaking glass,
But turned too late, I guess.
"Jimmy Lee did it," Artie said,
As we cleaned up the mess.

When Artie's room got painted,
Jimmy Lee was in the hall.
He used up Artie's crayons
Drawing pictures on the wall.

And when I finally found my bear,
I asked Artie, "Who hid it?"
He told me frankly, "Angel,
It was Jimmy Lee who did it."

He caused so much trouble
That I began to see —
The only way to stop it
Was to capture Jimmy Lee.

I knew about his sweet tooth,
So I set a tasty trap,
But Jimmy Lee just waited
Till I had to take my nap.

I spread out all my marbles
To trip up Jimmy Lee.
The dog slid by and scratched the floor
And Mom got mad at me.

I hid in the hall closet
And I never made a sound,
But Jimmy Lee will only come
When Artie is around.

I don't know what he looks like,
He never leaves a trace —
Except for spills and tears
And Artie's things about the place.

Since Artie won't describe him,
He remains a mystery.
But if you're smart, you'll listen
And watch out for Jimmy Lee.

Jimmy Lee
Who Could It Be?

Pat Cummings created a mystery story. The mystery was that things kept happening and Angel couldn't figure out who was causing them to happen.

You may want to write a mystery about your own life. Think about things that have happened to you that you couldn't figure out. Then share your mystery with a friend.

Meet Pat Cummings

Pat Cummings writes about people she knows and places she's been. Thinking about these things gives her ideas for stories.

The idea for the story *Jimmy Lee Did It* came from a make-believe friend that her brother had when he was little. This make-believe friend was always blamed for things that happened in the Cummings house.

Before Pat Cummings draws pictures for her books, she reads her stories to children. Then she asks them what they pictured in their minds. This helps her decide what pictures to draw.

Another book by Pat Cummings you may enjoy is *Clean Your Room, Harvey Moon!*

My Five Senses

by Aliki

I can see! I see with my eyes.

I can hear! I hear with my ears.

I can smell! I smell with my nose.

I can taste! I taste with my tongue.

I can touch! I touch with my fingers.

I do all this with my senses.

I have five senses.

When I see the sun or a frog

or my baby sister,
I use my sense of sight. I am seeing.

When I hear a drum or a fire engine
or a bird, I use my sense of hearing.
I am hearing.

When I smell soap or a pine tree or cookies
just out of the oven, I use my sense of smell.
I am smelling.

When I drink my milk and eat my food,
I use my sense of taste. I am tasting.

When I touch a kitten or a balloon or water,
I use my sense of touch. I am touching.

Sometimes I use all my senses at once.
Sometimes I use only one.
I often play a game with myself.
I guess how many senses I am using at that time.

When I look at the moon and the stars,
I use one sense. I am seeing.

When I laugh and play with my puppy,
I use four senses.
I see, hear, smell, and touch.

When I bounce a ball, I use three senses.
I see, hear, touch.

Sometimes I use more of one sense
and less of another.
But each sense is very important to me,
because it makes me aware.
To be aware is to see all there is to see . . .

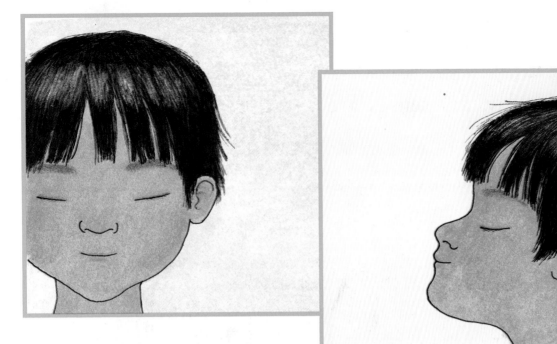

hear all there is to hear . . .

smell all there is to smell . . .

taste all there is to taste . . .

touch all there is to touch.

Wherever I go, whatever I do, every minute of the day, my senses are working.

They make me aware.

Look All Around You

What did you learn about your senses from Aliki's book?

Think about something that interests you and that you would like to learn more about. Then find some books about your interest.

After you have read the books, tell others about what you have learned. You might want to draw some pictures to make it more interesting for your listeners.

MEET ALIKI

Aliki uses only her first name on the books she writes and illustrates. Her whole name is Aliki Brandenberg. Her husband, Franz Brandenberg, also writes children's books, and she illustrates many of them.

Aliki at work in her garden

Aliki as a young girl

Some of Aliki's books are about imaginary people or animals. But others are about the lives of real people or about real, everyday things. Two books by Aliki that you might enjoy are *My Hands* and *Feelings*.

MARI'S TOOTH

by Alberto Barrera

It seems like only yesterday
My baby tooth was born.
It helped me bite and chew my way
Through rice and bread and corn.

For six whole years I ate and ate
My breakfast and my lunch.
And always cleaned my dinner plate —
My tooth loved every crunch.

Then *Abuelita* came to visit.
I couldn't eat her homemade bread.
She asked me then, "My dear, what *is* it?"
"My tooth is loose!" I said.

I bravely tugged and tugged and tugged.
I didn't cry and shout,
For *Mami* hugged and hugged and hugged,
And at last, I pulled it out!

That night I snuggled down in bed.
Soon Mr. Mouse would come.
He'd reach beneath my sleeping head
And take my tooth back home.

I said, "Goodbye, goodbye, old friend,
Dear tooth that helped me chew.
I'll wait and hope that in the end
My new tooth's just like you!"

MEET THE POET

Poets are authors who write poems. Alberto Barrera enjoys writing poems and songs for children — especially his own children.

Mr. Barrera grew up in a family that spoke Spanish, and he still writes his poems in that language. Some of his poems tell about experiences that he and his family have had.

The poem "Mari's Tooth" is about Mr. Barrera's daughter Mari and the loss of her first tooth. Other poems he has written tell what happened long ago in Rio Grande City, Texas, the town where he was born and still lives.

by George Shannon

illustrated by Jose Aruego and Ariane Dewey

Squirrel was worried.

His mother's birthday was one day away, and he still hadn't found her a present.

He had looked in all the stores in town,
but nothing seemed just right.
She had perfume and books and the most
beautiful garden.

He'd already given her drawings, and songs that he'd made up.

And every time he made a cake,

he burned it.

He sighed and said, "I'll just have to send her a plain old birthday card."
But as he was putting the stamp on, he had an idea.

He called his mother on the telephone and
said, "I'm sending you a package with a
surprise inside.
Be sure to open it right away."

The next day when the package arrived,
his mother took off the ribbons and opened
the box.

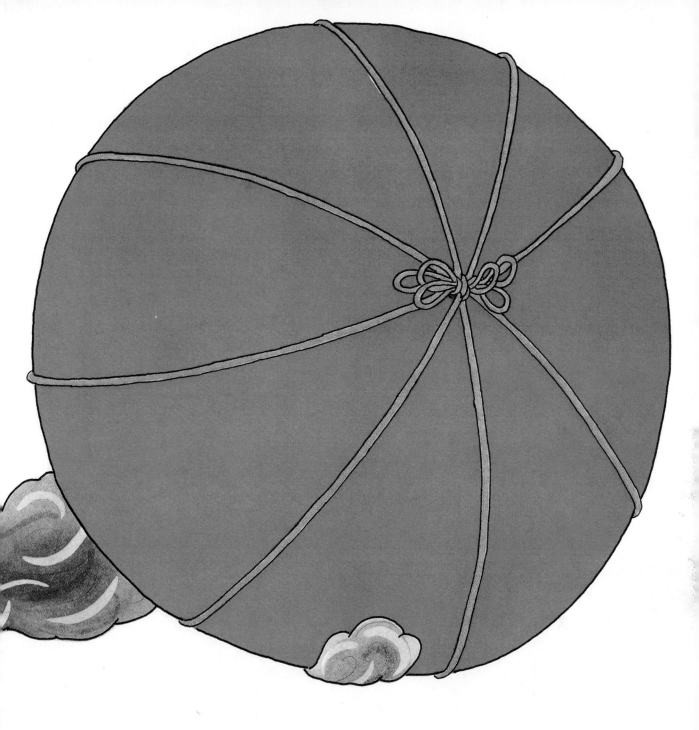

But there was only another box inside.

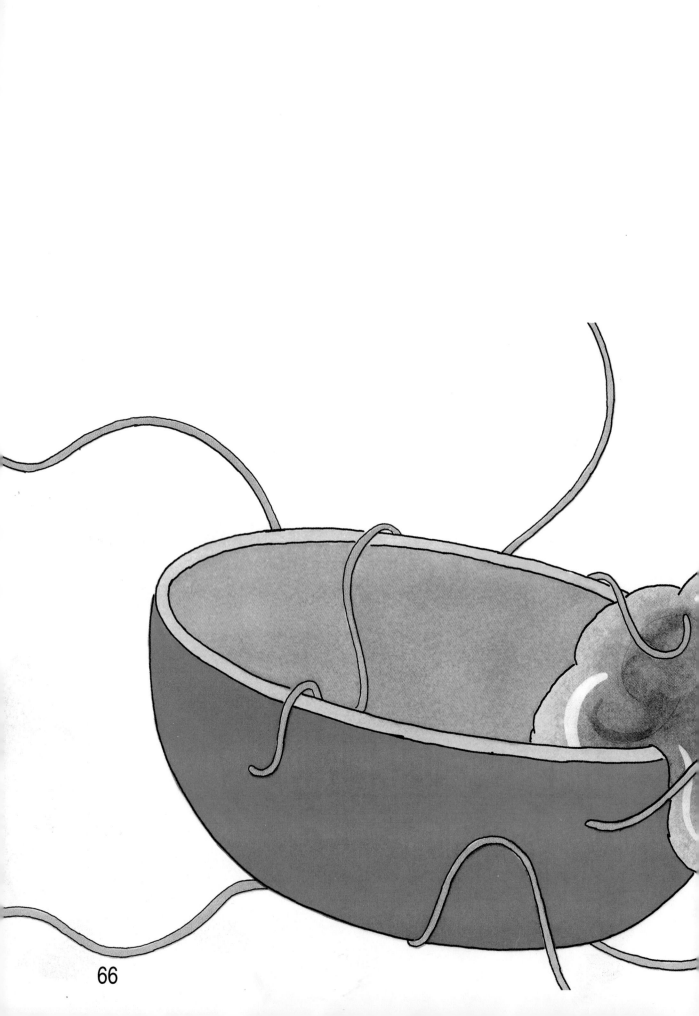

So she opened that box, and found another box.

And opened that box and found another box.

And opened that box, and found another box.

And when she opened that box . . .

Squirrel jumped out and gave her a kiss!

Keeping Secrets

When you found out what Squirrel's surprise for his mother was, were you surprised too?

Get together with some friends to plan your own short story with a surprise ending. Be ready to tell your story to other groups. You might want to write it down and make it into a book.

Dear Reading Friends,

Ideas for stories are everywhere, if we pay attention. Ideas can come from pictures, songs, and memories. From books, too. And always from people. What they do and how they feel.

Sometimes ideas come all in order like A B C D E F G. Other times they come mixed up and incomplete like C D F E G, without an A or B. I wrote the last part of *The Surprise* first! Then I kept asking myself questions. Why do people give gifts? When? How did Squirrel get the idea for this gift? How would I feel if I were Squirrel?

I write my stories over and over and over again. I add new words, take others out, and try different ideas. I work till each story sounds to me as smooth as singing the alphabet.

Best of writing and reading wishes.

George Shannon

Jose Aruego and Ariane Dewey worked together to make pictures for *The Surprise* and several other children's books. Jose drew the pictures, and Ariane added the color.

Jose Aruego says he grew up with many pets. His family had dogs, cats, horses, chickens, pigeons, frogs, and ducks! All the characters he draws for books are animals. He says that's because he can't draw people.

Ariane Dewey paints pictures for children's books. Ariane says she looks at colors everywhere she goes and uses many in her pictures.

WRITING WITH PICTURES

Jose Aruego and Ariane Dewey make pictures for storybooks. Here they show you how to get started — just in case you want to write a book of your own.

Jose says that for *The Surprise*, he first drew many small pictures of squirrels to help him decide how the characters in the story would look.

riane says she first went to the park to look at real squirrels. This helped her decide how to color in Jose's pictures.

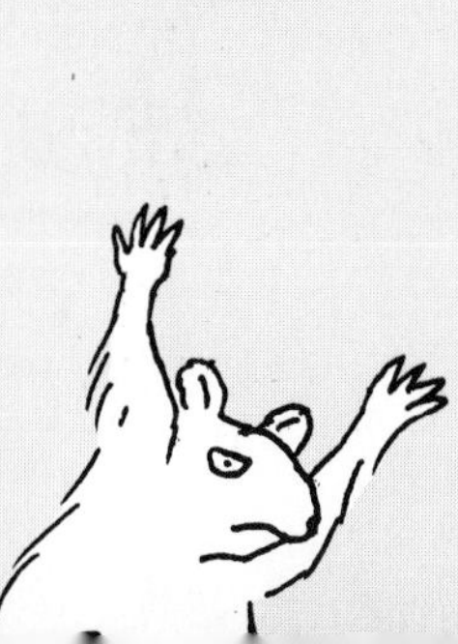

77

BOOKS BY FAVORITE AUTHORS

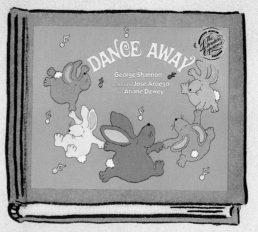

Dance Away

by George Shannon
Rabbit's friends are
too scared to move
— but Rabbit gets
them moving.

The Great Sea Monster

by Berthe Amoss
This author tells you
how she creates a
book about a sea
monster. Then she
shows you how *you*
can write a book.

My Visit to the Dinosaurs

by Aliki
Dinosaurs were
amazing animals.
Come along on a trip
to a museum to look
at dinosaur skeletons.

At Mary Bloom's

by Aliki
Mary Bloom has a
house full of animals.
But she is always
ready for more!

Old Favorites

Did you know that many of the rhymes, stories, and songs that you know are the same ones that your parents, grandparents, and even your great-grandparents enjoyed when they were your age?

Through the years these old stories, rhymes, and songs have been retold and reread over and over again because they're everybody's favorites.

81

Contents

Stone Soup   84
retold by Ann McGovern
illustrated by Cat Bowman Smith

The Three Little Pigs   106
retold and illustrated
by Paul Galdone

Baby Rattlesnake 128
told by Te Ata
adapted by Lynn Moroney
illustrated by Veg Reisberg

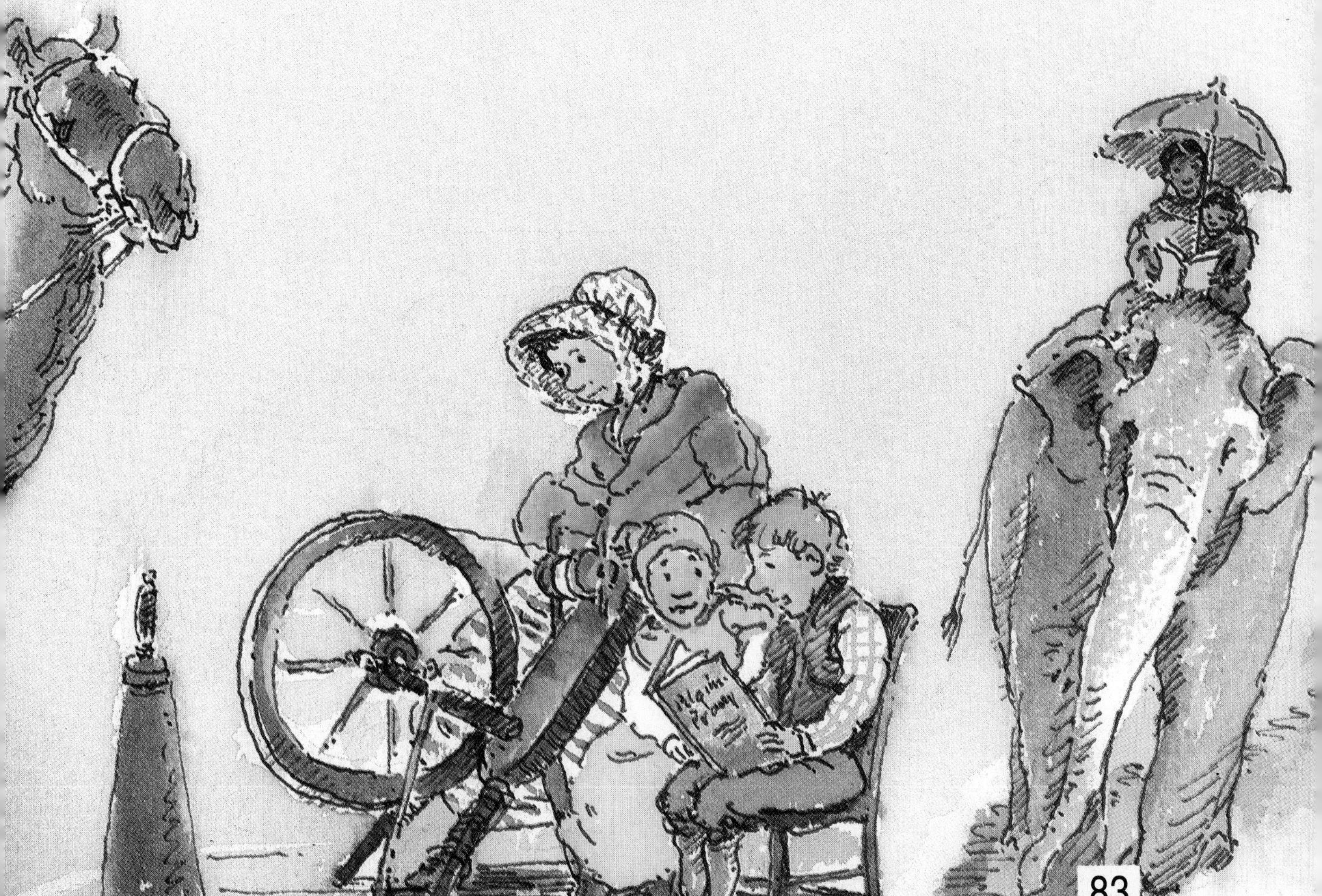

STONE

retold by Ann McGovern

SOUP

illustrated by Cat Bowman Smith

A young man was walking.
He walked and he walked.
He walked all night.
And he walked all day.

He was tired. And he was hungry.

At last he came to a big house.
"What a fine house," he said.
"There will be plenty of food
for me here."

He knocked on the door.
A little old lady opened it.

"Good lady," said the young man,
"I am very hungry.
Can you give me something to eat?"

"I have nothing to give you,"
said the little old lady.
"I have nothing in the house.
I have nothing in the garden."
And she began to close the door.

"Stop," said the young man.
"If you will not give me
    something to eat,
    will you give me a stone?"

"A stone?" said the little old lady.
"What will you do with a stone?
You cannot eat a stone!"

"Ah," said the young man.
"I can make soup from a stone."

Now the little old lady had
never heard of that.
Make soup from a stone?
Fancy that.

"There are stones in the road,"
said the little old lady.

The young man picked up a round,
gray stone.
"This stone will make wonderful soup,"
he said.
"Now get me a pot."

The little old lady got a pot.

"Fill the pot with water
and put it on the fire,"
the young man said.

The little old lady did as she was told.
And soon the water was bubbling
in the pot.

The young man put the round,
gray stone into the pot.
"Now we will wait for the stone to
cook into soup," he said.

The pot bubbled and bubbled.

After a while, the little old lady said,
"This soup is cooking fast."

"It is cooking fast now,"
said the hungry young man.
"But it would cook faster with
some onions."

So the little old lady went to the garden to get some yellow onions.

Into the pot went
the yellow onions,
with the round, gray stone.

"Soup from a stone,"
said the little old lady.
"Fancy that."

The pot bubbled and bubbled.

After a while, the little old lady said,
"This soup smells good."

"It smells good now,"
said the hungry young man.
"But it would smell better
with some carrots."

So the little old lady
went out to the garden
and pulled up all the carrots
she could carry.

Into the pot went
the long, thin carrots,
with the yellow onions,
and the round, gray stone.

"Soup from a stone,"
said the little old lady.
"Fancy that."

The pot bubbled and bubbled.

After a while, the little old lady said,
"This soup tastes good."

"It tastes good now,"
said the hungry young man.
"But it would taste better
with beef bones."

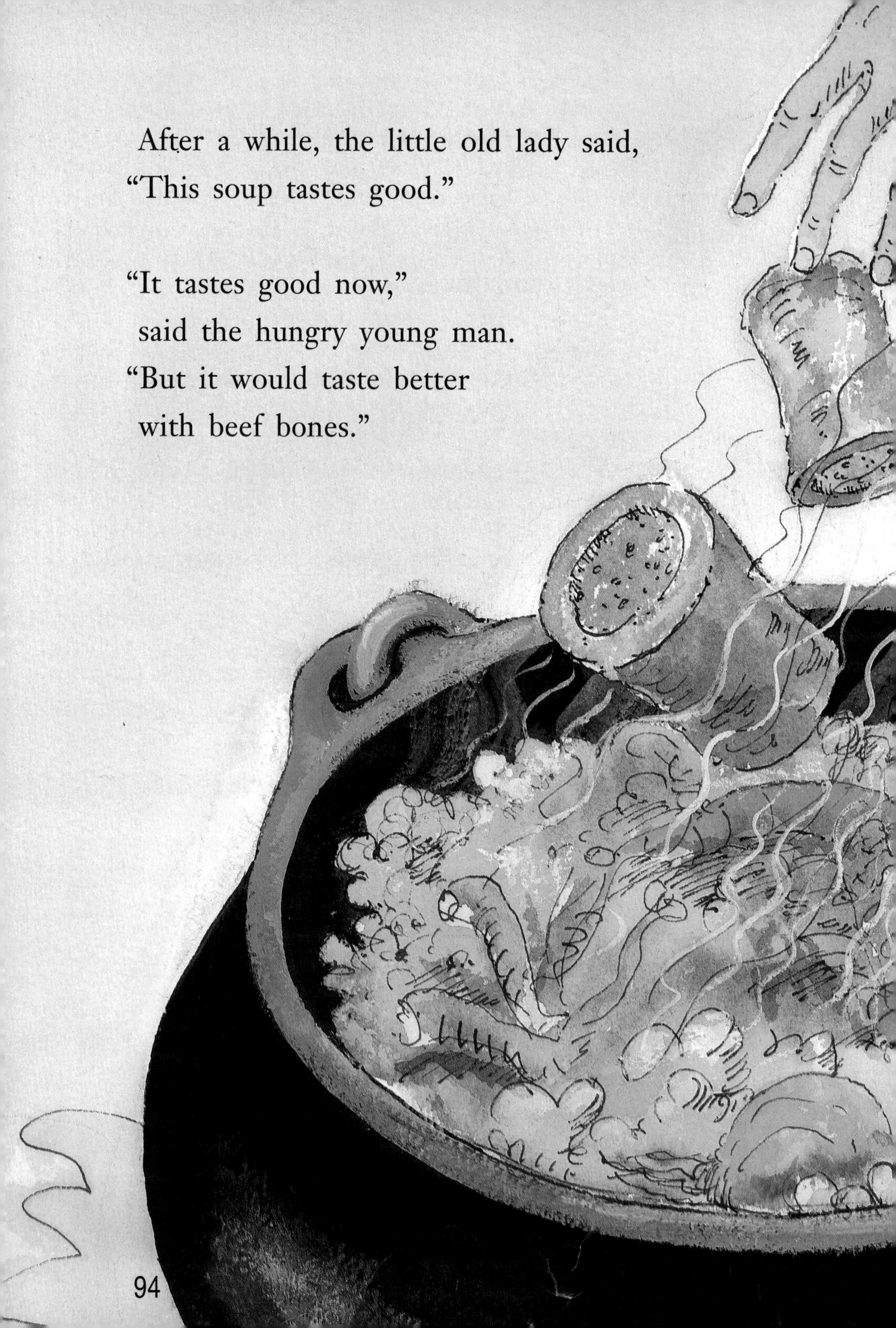

So the little old lady went to get
some juicy beef bones.

Into the pot went
the juicy beef bones,
and the long, thin carrots,
and the yellow onions,
and the round, gray stone.

"Soup from a stone,"
said the little old lady.
"Fancy that."

The pot bubbled and bubbled.

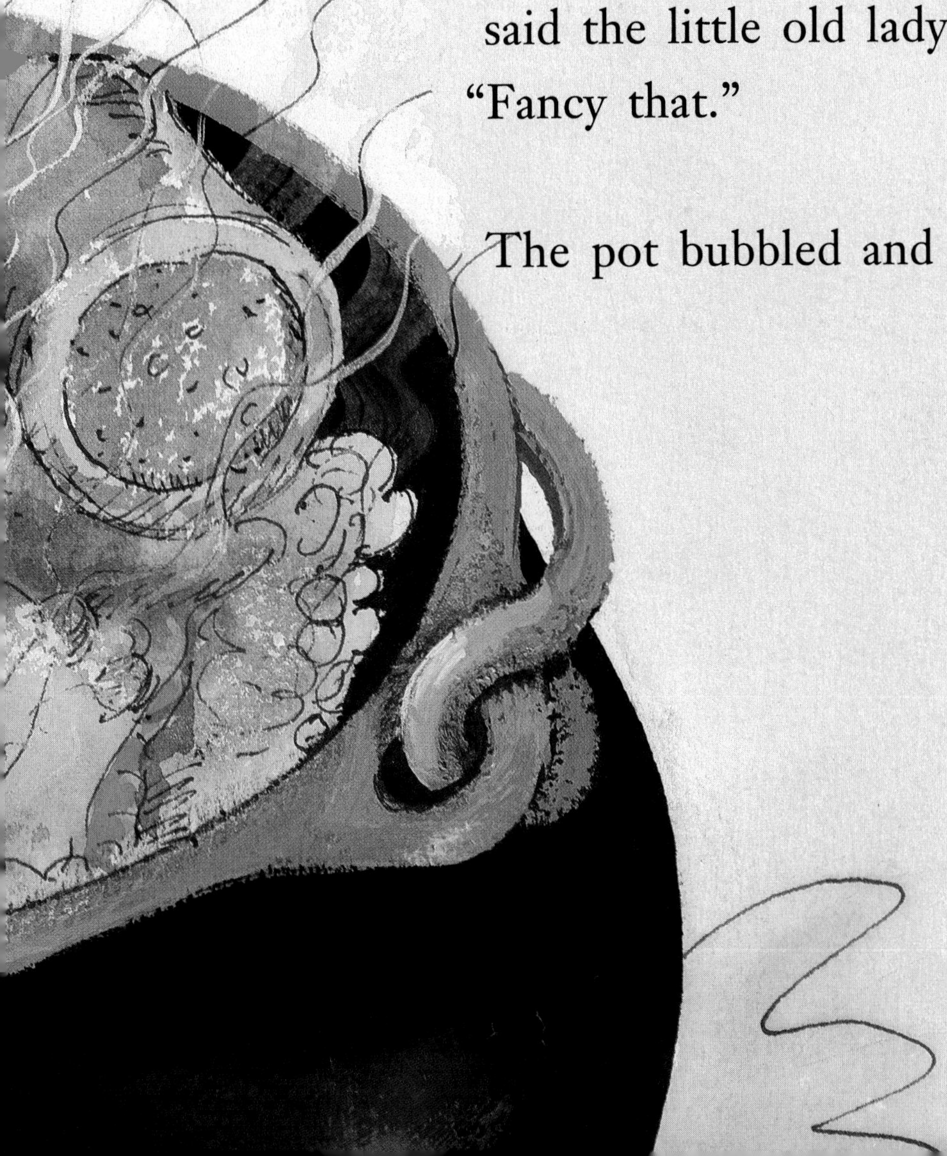

After a while, the little old lady said,
"This soup is fit for a prince."

"It is fit for a prince now,"
said the hungry young man.
"But it would be fit for a king
with a bit of pepper
and a handful of salt."

So the little old lady
got the pepper and the salt.

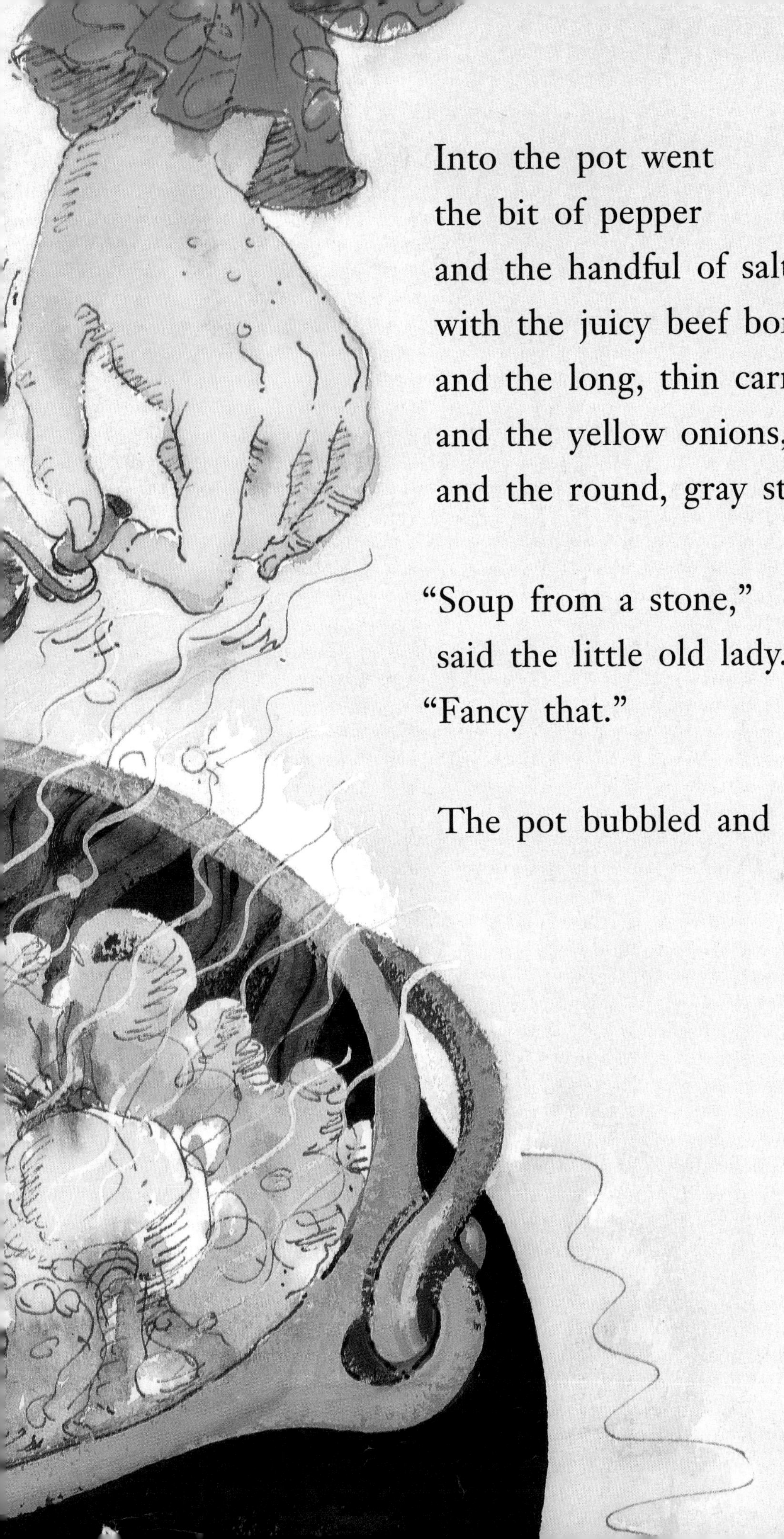

Into the pot went
the bit of pepper
and the handful of salt,
with the juicy beef bones,
and the long, thin carrots,
and the yellow onions,
and the round, gray stone.

"Soup from a stone,"
said the little old lady.
"Fancy that."

The pot bubbled and bubbled.

After a while, the little old lady said,
"This soup is too thin."

"It is too thin now,"
said the hungry young man.
"But it would be nice and thick
with some butter and barley."

So the little old lady
went to get butter and barley.

Into the pot went
the butter and barley,
with the bit of pepper
and the handful of salt,
and the juicy beef bones,
and the long, thin carrots,
and the yellow onions,
and the round, gray stone.

"Soup from a stone,"
said the little old lady.
"Fancy that."

The pot bubbled and bubbled.

After a while, the little old lady
tasted the soup again.
"That is good soup," she said.

"Yes," said the hungry young man.
"This soup is fit for a king.
Now we will eat it."

"Stop!" said the little old lady.
"This soup is indeed fit for a king.
Now I will set a table fit for a king."

So she took out her best
tablecloth and her best dishes.

Then the little old lady
and the hungry young man
ate all the soup —

the soup made with
the butter and barley,
and the bit of pepper,
and the handful of salt,
and the juicy beef bones,
and the long, thin carrots,
and the yellow onions,
and the round, gray stone.

"Soup from a stone,"
said the little old lady.
"Fancy that."

"Now I must be on my way,"
said the young man.
He took the stone out of the pot,
and put it into his pocket.

"Why are you taking the stone?"
said the little old lady.

"Well," said the young man.
"The stone is not cooked enough.
I will have to cook it some more
tomorrow."

And the young man said
good-bye.

He walked on down the road.
He walked and he walked.
"What a fine supper
I will have tomorrow,"
he said to himself.

"Soup from a stone.
Fancy that."

A Fine Supper For Tomorrow

Where do you think the young man might go next? Do you think he will find someone else who will help him make stone soup? Why?

With a friend, write a story that tells where you think the young man might go and what he might do. Draw a picture to help you tell your story.

Meet the Author

Ann McGovern writes many different kinds of books for children. She writes stories about famous people such as Christopher Columbus and Harriet Tubman. She writes about sharks, different kinds of sea life, and other science stories. She also writes new versions of old folktales, such as *Stone Soup*.

Meet the Illustrator

Cat Bowman Smith has had many different jobs as an illustrator. She began her work with a newspaper in New York. Later, she started drawing pictures for *Cricket*, a magazine for children. She has also illustrated several books for children, including *Princess Bee and the Royal Good-Night Story* by Sandy Asher.

Cat lives in Rochester, New York, with her husband. They have four grown children.

The Three Little Pigs

retold and illustrated

by Paul Galdone

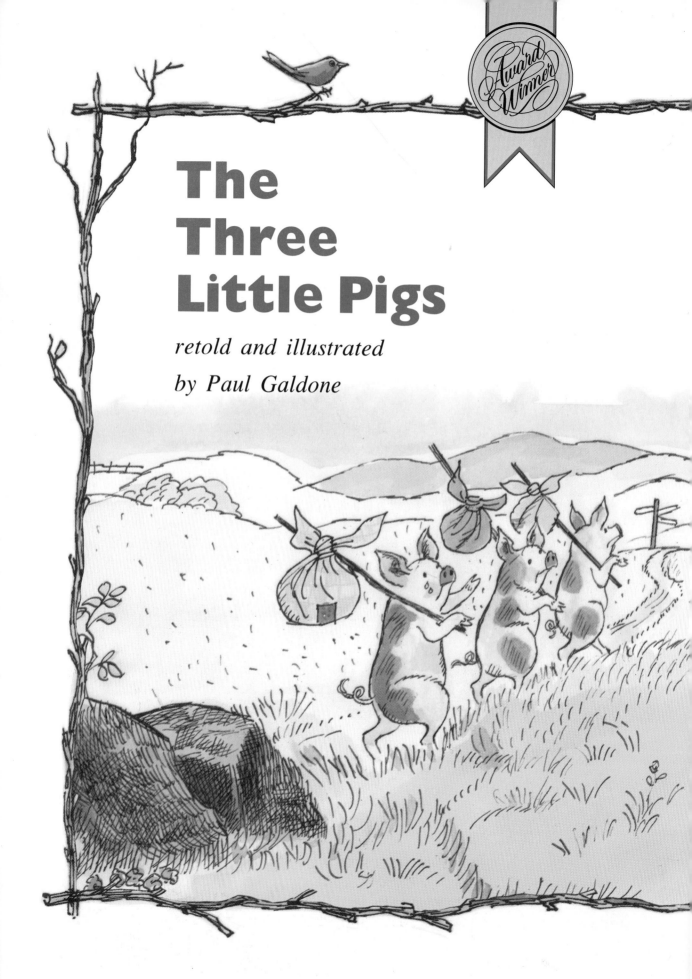

Once upon a time, there was an old sow with three little pigs. She had no money to keep them, so she sent them off to seek their fortune.

The first little pig met a man
with a bundle of straw,
and said to him:
"Please, man, give me that straw
to build me a house."

So the man did,
and the little pig
built his house with it.

Along came a wolf.
He knocked at the door, and said:
"Little pig, little pig, let me come in."

"No, no," said the little pig.
"Not by the hair of my
chinny chin chin."

"Then I'll huff, and I'll puff,
and I'll blow your house in,"
said the wolf.

So the wolf huffed, and he puffed,
and he blew the house in.
And he ate up the first little pig.

The second little pig met a man
with a bundle of sticks, and said:
"Please, man, give me those sticks
to build me a house."

So the man did,
and the little pig built
his house with them.

Then along came the wolf, and said:
"Little pig, little pig,
let me come in."

"No, no! Not by the hair
of my chinny chin chin."

"Then I'll huff, and I'll puff,
and I'll blow your house in,"
said the wolf.

So he huffed, and he puffed,
and he huffed and he puffed, and
at last he blew the house in.
And he ate up the second little pig.

The third little pig met a man
with a load of bricks, and said:
"Please, man, give me those bricks
to build me a house."

So the man did,
and the little pig built
his house with them.

Soon the same wolf
came along, and said:
"Little pig, little pig,
let me come in."

"No, no! Not by the hair
of my chinny chin chin."

"Then I'll huff, and I'll puff,
and I'll blow your house in,"
said the wolf.

Well, he huffed, and he puffed
and he huffed and he puffed
and he huffed and he puffed.

But he could *not* blow the house in.

At last the wolf stopped
huffing and puffing, and said:
"Little pig, I know where there is
a nice field of turnips."

"Where?" said the little pig.

"On Mr. Smith's farm," said the wolf.
"I will come for you tomorrow morning.
We will go together,
and get some turnips for dinner."

"Very well," said the little pig.
"What time will you come?"

"Oh, at six o'clock,"
said the wolf.

Well, the little pig got up at five.
He went to Mr. Smith's farm,
and got the turnips
before the wolf came to his house.

"Little pig, are you ready?"
asked the wolf.
The little pig said, "Ready!
I have been and come back again
and I got a nice potful of turnips
for my dinner."

The wolf was very angry.
But then he thought of
another way to get
the little pig, so he said:
"Little pig,
I know where there
is a nice apple tree."

"Where?" said the pig.

"Down at Merry Garden,"
  replied the wolf.
"I will come for you
  at five o'clock tomorrow morning
  and we will get some apples."

Well, the little pig got up
the next morning at four o'clock,
and went off for the apples.
He wanted to get back home
before the wolf came. But it was a
long way to Merry Garden,
and then he had to climb the tree.
Just as he was climbing back down
with his basket full of apples,
he saw the wolf coming!

"Little pig!" the wolf said.
"You got here before me!
Are the apples nice?"

"Yes, very," said the little pig.
"I will throw one down to you."
And he threw the apple as far
as he could throw.
While the wolf ran to pick it up,
the little pig jumped down and ran home.

The next day the wolf came again
and said to the little pig:
"Little pig, there is a fair at Shanklin
this afternoon. Would you like to go?"

"Oh, yes," said the little pig.
"When will you come to get me?"

"At three," said the wolf.

Well, the little pig went off at two o'clock
and bought a butter churn at the fair.

He was going home with it
when he saw the wolf coming!

The little pig jumped into the butter churn
to hide.

The churn fell over and rolled
down the hill with the little pig in it.
This frightened the wolf so much
that he turned around and ran home.

Later the wolf went to the little pig's house
and told him what had happened.

"A great round thing came rolling down the hill right at me," the wolf said.

"Hah, I frightened you then," said the little pig.

"I went to the fair and bought a butter churn. When I saw you, I got into it, and rolled down the hill."

The wolf was very angry indeed.
"I'm going to climb down your chimney
and eat you up!" he said.

When the little pig heard the wolf on the roof ~

he hung a pot
full of water in the fireplace.
Then he built a blazing fire.
Just as the wolf was coming down the chimney,
the little pig took the cover off the pot,
and in fell the wolf.
The little pig quickly put on the cover again,
boiled up the wolf, and ate him for supper.

And the little pig lived happily ever afterward.

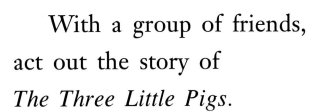

Let's do it again!

With a group of friends, act out the story of *The Three Little Pigs.* Use your own words and actions to retell the story. Be sure to make your voice sound like the voice of a pig or a wolf.

Perform your play with your friends.

Meet the Author and Illustrator

Before Paul Galdone became an author, he worked for a book publishing company. His job was to draw the pictures for other people's books. He soon decided that he would much rather draw pictures for his *own* books!

Mr. Galdone especially liked to retell and illustrate favorite old tales such as *The Three Little Pigs* and *The Three Billy Goats Gruff.* He also illustrated nursery rhymes and songs.

Can you imagine writing and illustrating almost two hundred books? Paul Galdone enjoyed making picture books so much that he did just that!

The Old Woman Who Lived In A Shoe

There was an old woman
Who lived in a shoe.
She had so many children
She didn't know what to do!

~ *anonymous*

Who's in the Shoe?

The Old Woman

You know the old woman
Who lived in a shoe?
And had so many children
She didn't know what to do?

I think if she lived in
A little shoe-house ~
That little old woman was
Surely a mouse!

by Beatrix Potter

127

BABY RATTLESNAKE

told by Te Ata
adapted by Lynn Moroney
illustrated by Veg Reisberg

Out in the place where the rattlesnakes lived, there was a little baby rattlesnake who cried all the time because he did not have a rattle.

He said to his mother and father, "I don't know why I don't have a rattle. I'm made just like my brother and sister. How can I be a rattlesnake if I don't have a rattle?"

Mother and Father Rattlesnake said, "You are too young to have a rattle. When you get to be as old as your brother and sister, you will have a rattle, too."

But Baby Rattlesnake did not want to wait.
So he just cried and cried. He shook his tail
and when he couldn't hear a rattle sound, he
cried even louder.

shhh! shhh! s
shhh! shhh

Mother and Father said, "Shhh! Shhh! Shhhhh!"

Brother and Sister said, "Shhh! Shhh! Shhhhh!"

But Baby Rattlesnake wouldn't stop crying. He kept the Rattlesnake People awake all night.

The next morning, the Rattlesnake People
called a big council. They talked and they
talked just like people do, but they couldn't
decide how to make that little baby rattlesnake
happy. He didn't want anything else but a
rattle.

At last one of the elders said, "Go ahead,
give him a rattle. He's too young and he'll get
into trouble. But let him learn a lesson. I just
want to get some sleep."

So they gave Baby Rattlesnake a rattle.
Baby Rattlesnake loved his rattle. He shook his
tail and for the first time he heard, "Ch-Ch-Ch!
Ch-Ch-Ch!" He was so excited!

He sang a rattle song, "Ch-Ch-Ch!
Ch-Ch-Ch!"

He danced a rattle dance, "Ch-Ch-Ch!
Ch-Ch-Ch!"

oon Baby Rattlesnake learned to play tricks with his rattle. He hid in the rocks and when the small animals came by, he darted out rattling, "Ch-Ch-Ch! Ch-Ch-Ch!"

He made Jack Rabbit jump. He made Old
Man Turtle jump. He made Prairie Dog jump.
Each time Baby Rattlesnake laughed and
laughed. He thought it was fun to scare the
animal people.

Mother and Father warned Baby Rattlesnake, "You must not use your rattle in such a way."

Big Brother and Big Sister said, "You are not being careful with your rattle."

The Rattlesnake People told Baby Rattlesnake to stop acting so foolish with his rattle.

Baby Rattlesnake did not listen.

One day, Baby Rattlesnake said to his mother and father, "How will I know a chief's daughter when I see her?"

"Well, she's usually very beautiful and walks with her head held high," said Father.

"And she's very neat in her dress," added Mother.

"Why do you want to know?" asked Father.

"Because I want to scare her!" said Baby Rattlesnake. And he started right off down the path before his mother and father could warn him never to do a thing like that.

The little fellow reached the place where the Indians traveled. He curled himself up on a log and he started rattling. "Chh-Chh-Chh!" He was having a wonderful time.

All of a sudden he saw a beautiful maiden coming toward him from a long way off. She walked with her head held high, and she was very neat in her dress.

"Ah," thought Baby Rattlesnake. "She must be the chief's daughter."

Baby Rattlesnake hid in the rocks. He was excited. This was going to be his best trick.

He waited and waited. The chief's daughter came closer and closer. When she was in just the right spot, he darted out of the rocks.

"Ch-Ch-Ch-Ch-Ch!"

"Ho!" cried the chief's daughter. She whirled around, stepping on Baby Rattlesnake's rattle and crushing it to pieces.

Baby Rattlesnake looked at his beautiful
rattle scattered all over the trail. He didn't
know what to do.

He took off for home as fast as he could.

With great sobs, he told Mother and Father what had happened. They wiped his tears and gave him big rattlesnake hugs.

For the rest of that day, Baby Rattlesnake stayed safe and snug, close by his rattlesnake family.

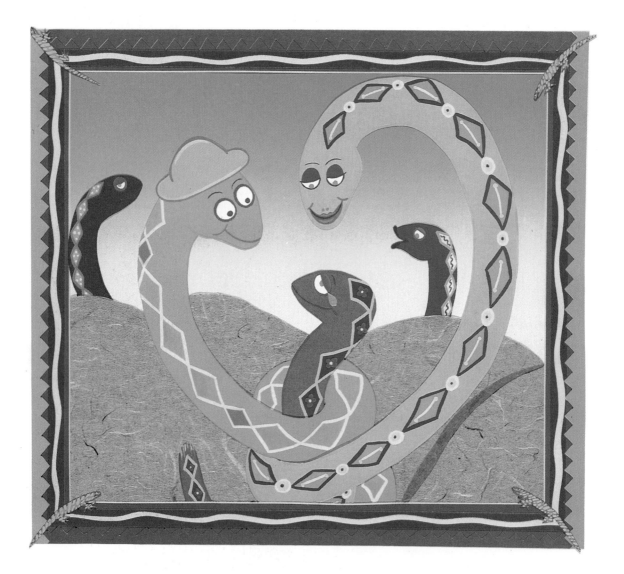

Baby Rattlesnake is an old favorite that was told for many years before it was written down. What is your favorite story?

Work with a partner. Tell each other your favorite stories. After you have listened to each other's stories, write them down. You might want to draw pictures for them, too.

Put the stories someplace in the classroom where others will be able to read and enjoy them also.

Te Ata, a Native American of the Chickasaw
people, has been a storyteller for more than
sixty-five years. She first heard some of the
stories she tells from her father. She has
traveled to many places telling her stories.

Lynn Moroney, who is also a storyteller, heard Te Ata telling stories. Ms. Moroney liked the story of Baby Rattlesnake so much that she wanted to write it down. Now that this story is a book, *Baby Rattlesnake* can be enjoyed by many more people.

MEET THE ILLUSTRATOR

Veg Reisberg is an artist who also loved the story about Baby Rattlesnake the first time she heard it. Ms. Reisberg used special watercolors and cut paper to make the pictures for *Baby Rattlesnake.*

On the top of a mountain
A grass blade was growing,
And up it a cricket was busily climbing.
I said to him, "Cricket,
Now where are you going?"
He answered me loudly, "I'm going out dining!"

Two little sisters went walking one day,
Partly for exercise, partly for play.
They took with them kites which they wanted
  to fly,
One a big centipede, one a great butterfly.
Then up in a moment the kites floated high,
Like dragons that seemed to be touching
  the sky!

— from *Chinese Mother Goose Rhymes*

This old lady, Hippity-hop,
Cut this piece of wood, flippity-flop.
She cut another,
She cut another,
She cut another,
She cut another, chippity-chop.
She gathered her wood, stick by stick,
And built a fire, flickity-flick.
A — black — cloud — grew.
The wet — rain — blew,
And she ran home, quickity-quick.

W e are little mice
   Out to dance and play.
We hope the cat of Don Tomás
   Will not come our way.

— from *Mother Goose on the Rio Grande*

Hickory, dickory, dock,

The mouse ran up the clock.

The clock struck one,

The mouse ran down,

Hickory, dickory, dock

Hey diddle diddle,

The cat and the fiddle;

The cow jumped over the moon.

The little dog laughed
To see such sport,

And the dish ran away with the spoon.

— from *Book of Nursery
and Mother Goose Rhymes*

More Old Favorites

Whale in the Sky

by Anne Siberell

In this folktale, Thunderbird watches over all creatures. But can he save them from Whale?

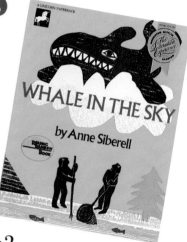

The Princess and the Pea

a Hans Christian Andersen tale

illustrated by Eve Tharlet

To find out how to tell if someone is a real princess, just read this old fairy tale.

Little Tuppen

retold and illustrated by Paul Galdone
Cluck-cluck! A hen rushes off to get water for her chick. But first she must find a cup to put it in.

Anansi the Spider: A Tale from the Ashanti

retold and illustrated by Gerald McDermott
Anansi, the famous spider of West Africa, has another adventure. This time he hopes his sons will help him get out of trouble.

Problems, problems!
Some problems may seem big,
and others may seem small.
Here are some stories and poems
about all kinds of problems!

CONTENTS

The Birthday Cake   160
written and illustrated by Ivar Da Coll

Carry Go Bring Come   190
by Vyanne Samuels
illustrated by Jennifer Northway

Anna's Secret Friend   216
by Yoriko Tsutsui
illustrated by Akiko Hayashi

The Birthday Cake

By Ivar Da Coll

*H*oratio the dog woke up. He thought about his friend Úrsula the hen. Úrsula's birthday had come and gone a little while ago, and Horatio had forgotten all about it!

Horatio packed some fruit into a basket.

*H*oratio hurried off to Úrsula's house. And there was Úrsula, pecking on her patio.

Horatio gave Úrsula a big hug and said, "This is for your birthday. I'm sorry I forgot."

"Don't worry," said Úrsula.
"Better late than never."

A kiss here, a kiss there,

      and Horatio went on his way.

All this talk about birthdays reminded Úrsula of her friend Eulalia the cow. Eulalia's birthday had come and gone a little while ago, and Úrsula had forgotten all about it!

Úrsula added four eggs to the basket of fruit.

Úrsula hurried off to Eulalia's house. And there was Eulalia, sweeping dry leaves from her yard.

Úrsula gave Eulalia a big hug and said, "This is for your birthday. I'm sorry I forgot."

"Don't worry," said Eulalia.
"Better late than never."

A kiss here, a kiss there,
and Úrsula went on her way.

All this talk about birthdays reminded Eulalia of her friend Camila the cat. Camila's birthday had come and gone a little while ago, and Eulalia had forgotten all about it!

Eulalia added cream, milk, and butter to the basket of fruit and eggs.

Eulalia hurried off to Camila's house. And there was Camila, sitting by her window.

Eulalia gave Camila a big hug and said, "This is for your birthday. I'm sorry I forgot."

"Don't worry," said Camila. "Better late than never."

A kiss here, a kiss there,
and Eulalia went on her way.

All this talk about birthdays reminded
Camila of her friend Ananías the duck.
Ananías's birthday had come and gone a
little while ago, and Camila had forgotten
all about it!

Camila added sugar to the basket of fruit,
eggs, cream, milk, and butter.

Camila hurried off to Ananías's house. And there was Ananías swimming in his pool.

Camila gave him a big hug and said, "This is for your birthday. I'm sorry I forgot."

"Don't worry," said Ananías. "Better late than never."

A kiss here, a kiss there,
      and Camila went on her way.

All this talk of birthdays reminded Ananías of his friend Eusebio the tiger. Eusebio's birthday had come and gone a little while ago, and Ananías had forgotten all about it!

The fruit had become a little mushed from all that packing, so Ananías made jam. He poured the jam into little jars and added them to the basket of eggs, cream, milk, butter, and sugar.

Ananías hurried off to Eusebio's house. And there was Eusebio combing his whiskers.

Ananías gave him a big hug and said, "This is for your birthday. I'm sorry I forgot."

"Don't worry," said Eusebio. "Better late than never."

A kiss here, a kiss there,
      and Ananías went on his way.

All this talk of birthdays did not remind Eusebio of anyone.

"I will bake myself a birthday cake," he said.

He went to the kitchen and put on his apron. And he carefully followed this recipe:

Sift a pound of flour into a bowl.
Add a pound of butter and mix slowly.
Add a dozen eggs, one at a time.
Add a pound of sugar and a tablespoon
of baking powder.
Pour into a pan and bake for 45 minutes
at 350 degrees.

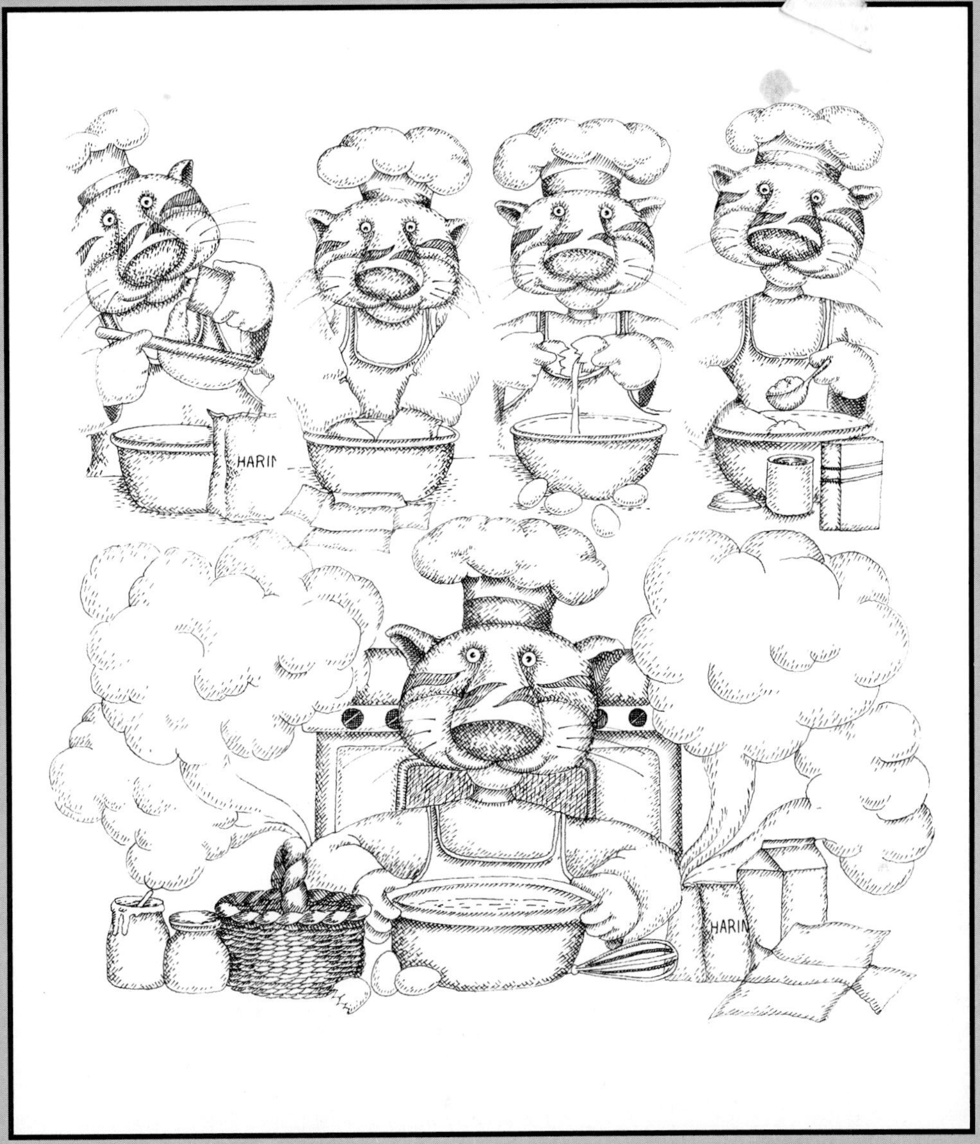
HARIN
HARIN

Soon the smell of the cake escaped through the open window and drifted through the air. Everyone sniffed. What a delicious smell!

The five friends headed toward the window. They could see Eusebio decorating the cake.

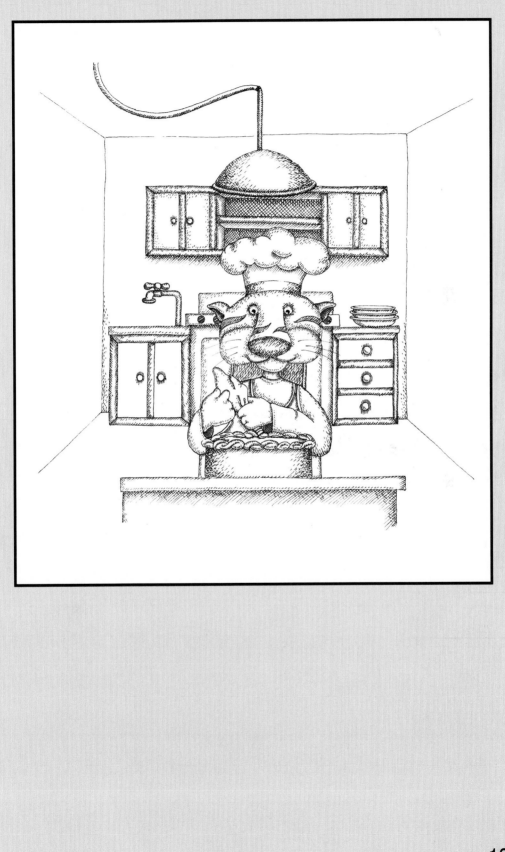

usebio took the cake into his dining room. Who do you think he found there? Horatio the dog, Úrsula the hen, Eulalia the cow, Camila the cat, and Ananías the duck — all were sitting at the table, smacking their lips.

"This is for all our birthdays, which we *all* forgot," they explained to Eusebio.

"Happy birthday to each of us," Eusebio replied.

A kiss here, a kiss there,
        and no one hurried off anywhere.

ANIMAL CHARACTERS

Ivar Da Coll has created many make-believe animal characters who act very much as people do. And they have problems, too — just as people do.

Create an animal character of your own and draw a picture of it. Give it a name. Then write about it and a problem it might have.

Poems About Everyday Problems

Whistling

Oh, I can laugh and I can sing
and I can scream and shout,
but when I try to whistle,
the whistle won't come out.

I shape my lips the proper way,
I make them small and round,
but when I blow, just air comes out,
there is no whistling sound.

But I'll keep trying very hard
to whistle loud and clear,
and some day soon I'll whistle tunes
for everyone to hear.

by Jack Prelutsky

187

A Problem

My zipper is stuck
    And what shall I do?
Give it a jerk
    And break it in two,
Give it a tug
    And then it will jam —
I think I'll just sit here
    The way that I am.

by Marchette Chute

Shoe Laces

Although I've tried and tried and tried,
I cannot keep my laces tied.
I really don't know what to do —

Unless I stick them tied with glue —
Except that such a sticky mess
Would not be good for shoes, I guess.

by Leland Jacobs

CARRY GO
BRING COME

by Vyanne Samuels

illustrated by Jennifer Northway

It was Saturday morning at Leon's house.
It was a big Saturday morning at Leon's house.
It was Marcia's wedding day. Marcia was Leon's
sister.

Everyone in the house was getting ready for
the big Saturday morning. Everyone was
getting ready for the big wedding.

Everyone, that is, except Leon, who was fast asleep downstairs.

"Wake up, Leon!" shouted his mother upstairs.

But Leon did not move.

"Wake up, Leon!" shouted his sister Marlene upstairs.

But Leon did not move.

Leon's mother and his sisters, Marlene and Marcia, were so busy taking big blue rollers out of their hair that they forgot to shout at Leon to wake up again.

They were getting ready for the big day.
They were getting ready for Marcia's wedding.

"Wake up, Leon," said Grandma softly
downstairs.

Leon's two eyes opened up immediately.
Leon was awake.

"Carry this up to your mother," said
Grandma, handing him a pink silk flower.

Leon ran upstairs to the bedroom with the pink silk flower. But before he could knock on the door, his sister Marcia called to him.

"Wait a little," she said, and she handed him a white veil. "Carry this down to Grandma."

So Leon put the flower between his teeth
and the veil in his two hands and ran down the
stairs to Grandma.

When he got to his grandma's door, she
called to him before he could knock.

"Wait a little," she said. He waited.

"Carry these up to Marlene," she said, and
she poked a pair of blue shoes out at him.

So Leon put the veil on his head, kept the flower between his teeth, and carried the shoes in his two hands.

He tripped upstairs to Marlene.

But when he got to the bedroom door,
Marlene called to him before he could knock.

"Wait a little," she said, and she poked a
pair of yellow gloves through the door. "Carry
these down to Grandma."

So Leon put the
gloves on his hands,

the shoes on his feet,

the veil on his head,
and the pink silk flower
between his teeth.

He wobbled downstairs to Grandma, who called to him before he could knock.

"Wait a little," she said. He waited.

"Carry this to Marcia," she said, and she poked a green bottle of perfume through the door.

"Mind how you go," she said.

So Leon climbed the stairs carefully holding the green bottle of perfume, carefully wearing the yellow gloves, carefully dragging the blue shoes, carefully balancing the white veil, carefully biting the pink silk flower . . . when suddenly he could go no further and shouted, "HELP!" from the middle of the stairs.

He nearly swallowed the flower.

His mother ran out of the room upstairs, his sister Marlene ran out of the room upstairs, and Grandma rushed out of her room downstairs.

There was a big silence. They all looked
at Leon.

"Look 'pon his feet!" said his mother.

"Look 'pon his fingers and his hands!" said Marlene.

"Look 'pon his head!" said Grandma.

"Look 'pon his mouth!" said Marcia.

And they all let go a big laugh!

Leon looked like a bride!

One by one, Mother, Marcia, Marlene, and Grandma took away the pink silk flower, the white veil, the green bottle of perfume, the blue shoes, and the yellow gloves.

"When am I going to get dressed for the wedding?" asked Leon, wearing just his pajamas now.

"Just wait a little!" said Grandma.

Leon's two eyes opened wide.

"YOU MEAN I HAVE TO WAIT A LITTLE?" he shrieked.

And before anyone could answer, he ran downstairs . . .

and jumped straight back into his bed, without waiting even a little.

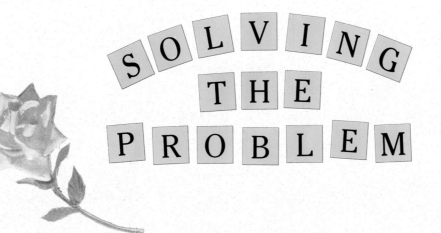

SOLVING THE PROBLEM

Leon ended up doing too many things at one time. How did he solve his problem?

Write a letter to Leon and tell him about a problem you had and how you solved it.

HICCUPS AND SNEEZES

Hiccups and sneezes are problems just about *every* body has had. But did you ever wonder what a hiccup is or why you sneeze?

Read on to find out all about these funny things your body does.

Those Darn Hiccups!

Hiccups happen when a muscle in your body tightens up when it shouldn't.

- This muscle is called the diaphragm (die-a-fram).
- It is between your chest and your stomach.
- It helps you breathe.
- It tightens when you breathe in.
- It relaxes when you breathe out.
- Sometimes it tightens when it shouldn't.
- Nobody knows why.
- But when it does, a flap of skin in your throat drops down.
- This flap stops air from getting in.
- The air hits the flap — "Hic!"

Flap

Lungs

Diaphragm

Hiccup, hiccup, go away!
Come again another day;
Hiccup, hiccup, when I bake,
I'll give to you a butter-cake.
— *Mother Goose*

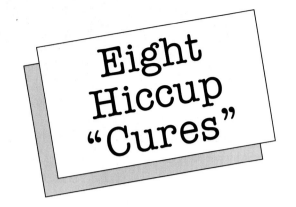

Eight Hiccup "Cures"

Next time you get the hiccups, try one of these "cures." Who knows? It might even work!

Drink a large glass of water.

Get someone to scare you.

Stand on your head.

Swallow ten times.

Eat peanut butter.

$1 - 2 - 3 - 4 - 5$
$6 - 7 - 8 - 9 \ldots$

Breathe into a paper bag.

Hold your breath and count to ten.

Take a hot bath.

Aaaah...choo!

Something tickles your nose.

It may be dust
or a peppery smell.

This makes you suck in
air through your mouth —

Aaaah . . .

Air blasts out your
mouth and nose — **choo!**

Out comes whatever was
bothering your nose.

That's what sneezes are for.

Anna's Secret Friend

by Yoriko Tsutsui
illustrated by Akiko Hayashi

Anna was excited about moving to a
new house in a new town. She was
especially pleased to be living close to
the mountains. But already she was
missing the friends she had left behind.

Still, there was hardly time to think
about anything because there were so
many boxes to be carried into the
new house.

Soon every room was full of boxes.
Anna began to help unpack, but before
long she was bored and tired.

Suddenly she heard a quiet tip tap
sound. The noise came from
the front door.

"I heard the postman," said Anna.
"I don't think it could have been,"
said her mother.
"We haven't told anyone our new
address yet," said her father.
"But I *did* hear someone," said Anna,
and she went to look.

At the front door Anna saw that her mother and her father were right. There were no letters, but there was something much nicer — a small bunch of violets that lay on the floor. How did the pretty flowers get there?

Quickly Anna opened the front door
to see who could have brought the
flowers. But all she could see was an
unfamiliar street, and lots of people she
hadn't seen before walking by.

Next morning Anna's mother did more unpacking. "I just don't know who could have given those violets to us yesterday," she said to Anna.

Just then, Anna heard that noise again — a quiet tip tap sound at the front door.

Anna ran to the front door. This time
there were three dandelions in the
letter box. Anna carefully picked out
the yellow flowers and opened the
front door. But once again all she saw
were people she didn't know walking
along the street.

The next day Anna went shopping with her mother. It was very strange to be going into new shops and seeing people she didn't know. She wished her old friends were not so far away.

"Just look at those magnificent mountains," said her mother. "I'm sure we're going to love living in this town."

"Who do you think could have left those dandelions yesterday?"
Anna asked.

"Maybe they were left for someone who lived in the house before us. Perhaps a little girl's friends don't know she has moved away," answered her mother.

The house was nearly tidy the next day, but Anna's mother was still busy.

Anna drew a picture to send to one of her old friends.

"It's no fun without any friends to play with," she said sadly.
But what was that? Anna heard the same quiet tip tap sound!

Anna rushed to the letter box, and this time she saw a letter in it! There was no name on the envelope, but inside there was a short message written in big letters.

Friends are nice
I'm very happy you have come
I'll be waiting

Anna read the letter again and again. "I'm sure this letter is for me," she thought.

Anna enjoyed visiting her new school.
A friendly teacher showed her all the
toys the children played with, and told
her about the meadow at the foot of
the mountains where the children
sometimes played.

"You'll soon make lots of new friends," the teacher told Anna. Anna looked at all the children laughing and chattering in the playground. She hoped that one of them had sent her the letter.

"Violets, dandelions, a letter . . .
Violets, dandelions, a letter . . . "
Anna sang as she played marbles by
herself. How she longed for someone
to play with!

Just then she heard that sound
again — a quiet little tip tap noise at
the front door.

"Wait! Wait!" Anna shouted in her loudest voice as she rushed to the front door. She saw something coming through the letter box! It was a beautiful paper doll.

Anna grabbed the doll and quickly opened the door. She saw a little girl just going out of the gate.
"Wait! Wait!" Anna shouted again.

The little girl turned around slowly. Her cheeks were bright red.

Anna walked down the path.

"Those violets — were they for me?"
she asked.

The little girl nodded.

"And . . . and the letter? Was that for
me too?" Once again the little girl
nodded.

Anna looked down at the beautifully
folded paper doll in her hand.

All for her! The little girl looked at
Anna shyly and said in a very small
voice, "Will you play with me?"

This time it was Anna who nodded, so
both girls smiled happily and went off
to play.

How To Make Friends

Anna was new in her neighborhood and her school. If there was a new person in your neighborhood or class, how could you help that person feel more at home?

Write your ideas down and make a how-to book called "How To Be a Friend." Draw pictures to illustrate your ideas. Then share your how-to book with a friend.

Meet the Authors and Illustrators

Ivar Da Coll lives in Bogotá, Colombia, with his two cats, Sara and Eusebio. The three of them enjoy cooking and listening to music together.

Ivar Da Coll has written and illustrated other books about Eusebio and his friends. These animal characters also have appeared on television and in the theater.

Vyanne Samuels went to college in both England and the United States. She also taught school in both countries — and in Jamaica, an island country in the Caribbean. Mrs. Samuels now lives in Jamaica with her husband and son.

Jennifer Northway spent most of her childhood in Africa. But like Vyanne Samuels, the author, she also went to college in England. Mrs. Northway has lived in several island countries in the Caribbean.

Yoriko Tsutsui lives in Japan with her husband and three daughters. This author writes in Japanese, but some of her stories are printed in English for English-speaking children to enjoy.

Akiko Hayashi has illustrated many books by Yoriko Tsutsui and other authors. She has also written and illustrated many children's books of her own.

More Problems to Solve!

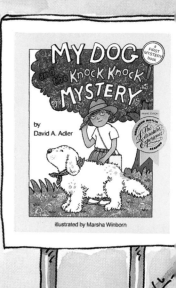

My Dog and the Knock Knock Mystery
by David A. Adler

Jennie's friend Billy is bothered by a mysterious knocking. Luckily Jennie's dog is a detective.

Jamaica Tag-Along *by Juanita Havill*

Jamaica can't understand why her big brother doesn't want her to tag along after him. Then someone begins to tag along after her.

Runaway Mittens *by Jean Rogers*

Pica's special red mittens are always disappearing! Can you guess how the problem of the missing mittens is solved?

Hemi's Pet *by Joan de Hamel*

Hemi's problem is that he doesn't have a pet. So how can he be in his school pet show without one?

235

What's for Lunch?

Thinking It Over

How do you get the energy to do the things you do?

Key Words

body

energy

fuel

Think about all the things you do every day. You walk, run, eat, drink, work, and play. You talk, listen, read, and think. All of that takes **energy**!

The food you eat helps your **body** make the energy that you need.

In this lesson you will learn how your body uses food to make energy. You will also learn about some foods that give you energy, help you grow, and keep you healthy.

There's the bell! It's time for lunch.

Alex goes to the school cafeteria to eat. He takes a peanut butter sandwich out of his lunch box. He starts to munch his lunch. Alex's body goes right to work. It's changing the food he is eating into **fuel.**

Fuel is something that is used to make energy. The fuel that makes a car go is gas. The fuel that makes a campfire burn is wood.

The fuel that will give Alex energy to play kickball at recess is a peanut butter sandwich!

Stop and Think

1. What does your body use for fuel?
2. What does your body do with its fuel?

Two of Alex's friends are sitting near him in the cafeteria. Susie and Carlos have been working hard all morning, and they are very hungry!

Susie is eating a bean burrito with rice. She also has a carton of apple juice and an oatmeal cookie.

The oats in the oatmeal cookie and the rice are grains. Grains are one of the best kinds of food for energy. Bread and cereal are made from grains.

Carlos has brought a tuna fish sandwich.
He also has carrots, a banana, and a
carton of milk.

The tuna sandwich and the milk will help
Carlos's body grow. Fish and milk are
good foods for strong muscles and bones.
The carrots and the banana will also help
Carlos. Vegetables and fruits are
important for keeping him healthy and
free from problems like colds and the flu.

Now Alex, Susie, and Carlos are ready
for recess.

Stop and Think

1. Name your favorite grains, fruits, and vegetables.
2. How do Alex, Susie, and Carlos use the energy
   they got from eating lunch?

SUSIE burrito
apple juice
oatmeal cookie
ALEX

Alex, Susie, and Carlos return to their classroom after recess. They find their teacher, Ms. Chang, writing something on the board. Ms. Chang wants to make a list of foods that some of the children ate for lunch.

When it is finished, the list looks like this.

SUSIE   burrito
apple juice
oatmeal cookie

ALEX   peanut butter sandwich
orange juice
pretzels

CARLOS   tuna fish sandwich
carrots
banana
milk

MIMI   cheese sandwich
grape juice

What do you like to eat for lunch?

This page will show you how to make a list of the foods you eat for lunch. Use another sheet of paper to write your name, the days of the week, and the foods you eat for lunch each day.

Tuesday lunch
- turkey sandwich
- milk
- pear
- chips

Review

1. How do people get energy to do all the things they do?

2. What are the kinds of foods that your body needs?

Glossary

A

attach   When you **attach** things, you put them together: Tim is **attaching** a basket to his bicycle so he will be able to carry his books.

B

birthday   Jenny is seven years old. She will be eight on her next **birthday**.

bricks   **Bricks** are made from clay. They are used in buildings, walkways, and walls: Tim's father made their house of **bricks**.

bubbling   The water in the pot is **bubbling** because it is very hot.

build   When you **build** a house, you make a house: I like to watch the workers **build** the new house on our street.

capture   When you **capture** something, you catch it: The police will **capture** the robbers and put them in jail.

chimney   A **chimney** is part of a house: When you have a fire in your fireplace, the smoke goes out the **chimney**.

combing   A **comb** is a long, thin tool that you run through your hair to make it neat: Danny is **combing** his hair before his picture is taken.

describe When you **describe** something, you tell what it looks like: Pat doesn't know what your dog looks like. Can you **describe** it to her?

dozen When you have a **dozen** things, you have twelve: We bought a **dozen** eggs at the store.

E

envelope You put a letter into an **envelope** before you mail it: Danny put an address and a stamp on the **envelope**.

escaped When something **escapes**, it gets away or gets out: We **escaped** from the angry dog. The sound of barking **escaped** from the window.

especially Joan is very happy that today is Saturday. She is **especially** happy because today is her birthday.

fancy People might say "**Fancy** that!" instead of "Can you believe that!" or "Imagine that!": In the story, a man makes soup from a stone. Can you **fancy** that?

floor   The **floor** is the part of a room that you walk on: Hank is cleaning the kitchen **floor**.

grabbed   When you **grab** something, you take it quickly: Anna **grabbed** the doll out of the mailbox.

guess   You can **guess** the answer to the question or riddle even if you do not know it.

huff   When you **huff**, you blow out a big breath: Lisa **huffed** and **huffed** to blow out the candles.

idea An **idea** is a thought: At first Jack didn't know what to do. But then he had a great **idea**!

important Pete wants very much to run in the race. Running in the race is **important** to him.

juicy These are **juicy** oranges. Maybe we can make orange juice from them.

knock John **knocked** at the door. Sue heard him **knock** and let him in.

lesson A **lesson** is something that you learn: When we got wet, we learned a **lesson** — carry our umbrellas on a cloudy day.

load A **load** is a big pile of something: We put a big **load** of hay in the barn for the cows.

marbles **Marbles** are small, round balls made of stone or glass. They are used in games: Jerry played a game of **marbles** with Sharon.

message   A **message** can be a short letter, a note, or something that someone tells you: Fred wrote me a **message**. He asked me to meet him at the park on Monday.

minute   You use **minutes** to tell the time: "What time is it?" asked Carlos. "It is one **minute** past five," said Tom.

mountains   **Mountains** are very high hills: We hiked up to the top of the **mountain** and looked down. Everything below looked so small!

mystery   A **mystery** is something that is not known: Margo's coat just disappeared! What happened to it is a **mystery**.

nothing   Pat looked at a lot of clothes in the store, but she saw **nothing** she liked. So she didn't buy anything at all.

open   The box is closed. What do you think we will see when we **open** it?

package   Nancy got a big **package** in the mail. She opened it to see what was inside.

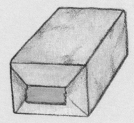

pajamas   **Pajamas** are a set of shirt and pants that you wear to bed: Sam wore his blue **pajamas** last night.

quiet   When you are **quiet**, you make almost no sound.

replied   When you **reply,** you give an answer to a question: "What day is today?" asked Tim. "It's Monday," **replied** Beth.

rushed   When you **rush,** you do something in a hurry or move in a hurry: We were in a hurry to meet Grandma as she got off the train. We ran as we **rushed** through the train station.

S

scattered   The puzzle pieces were **scattered** all around the rug. Some pieces were under the chair, and some more were under the table.

straw   **Straw** looks like dry grass or stems: Hats and baskets can be made from **straw.**

tomorrow   The day after today is **tomorrow:** Today is Friday. There is no school **tomorrow** because it is Saturday.

tongue   You have a **tongue** in your mouth. You use your **tongue** when you eat and when you talk.

trail   A **trail** is a path that people or animals can walk along: We walked down the **trail** to the cabin in the woods.

trouble　My puppy behaves most of the time. When she doesn't behave and causes lots of **trouble,** I send her to the doghouse.

unfamiliar　Tim had never been to the city. He had never seen tall buildings or crowds of people before. The city looked strange and **unfamiliar** to him.

violets　**Violets** are flowers: Sam bought some purple **violets** at the plant store.

warn   The smoke alarm will **warn** us if a fire starts in the house.

whirled   When something **whirls,** it spins around quickly: The top made a little hum as it **whirled** around.

wolf   A **wolf** is a wild animal that looks like a dog.

young   Sara is **young.** She is only two years old.

zoo   A **zoo** is a park where people go to see animals: You might see lions, elephants, or bears at the **zoo**.

Acknowledgments

For each of the selections listed below, grateful acknowledgment is made for permission to excerpt and/or reprint original or copyrighted material, as follows:

Major Selections

Anna's Secret Friend, by Yoriko Tsutsui, illustrated by Akiko Hayashi. Text copyright © 1986 by Yoriko Tsutsui. Illustrations copyright © 1986 by Akiko Hayashi. Reprinted by permission of Viking Penguin (a division of Penguin Books USA, Inc.), and Fukuinkan Shoten, Publishers, Inc.

Baby Rattlesnake, told by Te Ata, adapted by Lynn Moroney, illustrated by Veg Reisberg. Published by Children's Book Press. Story copyright © 1989 by Lynn Moroney. Illustrations copyright © 1989 by Veg Reisberg. Reprinted by permission of GRM Associates, Inc., Agents for Children's Book Press.

The Birthday Cake (*Torta de Cumpleanos*), by Ivar Da Coll. Copyright © 1989. Translated and reprinted by permission of Carlos Valencia Editores, S.A.

Carry Go Bring Come, by Vyanne Samuels, illustrated by Jennifer Northway. Text copyright © 1989 by Vyanne Samuels. Illustrations copyright © 1989 by Jennifer Northway. Reprinted by permission of Four Winds Press (an imprint of Macmillan Publishing Company), and The Bodley Head Ltd.

Jimmy Lee Did It, by Pat Cummings. Copyright © 1985 by Pat Cummings. Reprinted by permission of Lothrop, Lee and Shepard Books (a division of William Morrow and Co., Inc.).

My Five Senses, by Aliki (Thomas Y. Crowell). Copyright © 1962, 1989 by Aliki Brandenberg. Reprinted by permission of Harper and Row, Publishers, Inc.

Stone Soup, by Ann McGovern. Text copyright © 1968 by Ann McGovern. Reprinted by permission of Scholastic, Inc.

The Surprise, by George Shannon, illustrated by Jose Aruego and Ariane Dewey. Text copyright © 1983 by George Shannon. Illustrations copyright © 1983 by Jose Aruego and Ariane Dewey. Reprinted by permission of Greenwillow Books (a division of William Morrow and Co., Inc.) and Julia MacRae Books.

The Three Little Pigs, by Paul Galdone. Copyright © 1970 by Paul Galdone. Reprinted by permission of Clarion Books/Ticknor and Fields, a Houghton Mifflin Company.

Poetry

"Mari's Tooth," by Alberto Barrera. Reprinted by permission of the author.

"The Old Woman," from *Appley Dappley's Nursery Rhymes* by Beatrix Potter. Copyright © 1917 by Frederick Warne and Co. Reprinted by permission of Frederick Warne and Co.

"On the top of a mountain…" from *Chinese Mother Goose Rhymes*, selected and edited by Robert Wyndham. Copyright © 1968 by Robert Wyndham. Reprinted by permission of Philomel Books.

"A Problem," from *Rhymes About Us* by Marchette Chute. Copyright © 1974 by E. P. Dutton. Reprinted by permission of Mary Chute Smith.

"Shoe Laces," from *Is Somewhere Always Far Away?* by Leland Jacobs. Copyright © 1967 by Leland B. Jacobs. Reprinted by permission of Henry Holt and Company, Inc.

"This old lady, Hippity-hop, . . ." from *Mother Goose on the Rio Grande* by Frances Alexander. Copyright © 1977, 1988 by Passport Books (a division of NTC Publishing Group). Reprinted by permission of Passport Books.

"Two little sisters…" from *Chinese Mother Goose Rhymes*, selected and edited by Robert Wyndham. Copyright © 1968 by Robert Wyndham. Reprinted by permission of Philomel Books.

"We are little mice. . . ." from *Mother Goose on the Rio Grande* by Frances Alexander. Copyright © 1977, 1988 by Passport Books (a division of NTC Publishing Group). Reprinted by permission of Passport Books.

"Whistling," from *Rainy Rainy Saturday* by Jack Prelutsky. Copyright © 1980 by Jack Prelutsky. Reprinted by permission of Greenwillow Books (a division of William Morrow and Co., Inc.).

Credits

Program Design   Carbone Smolan Associates

Cover Design   Carbone Smolan Associates

Design   10–79 Maria Perez/Design;   80–155 WGBH; 156–159, 187–189, 216–231, 234–235 DeFrancis Studio; 160–186, 190–215, 232–233 Luis Tomas;   236–241 Pronk & Associates

Introduction   (left to right) 1st row: Cameron Gerlach Studio; C. Moore/The Image Bank; Chris Demarest;   2nd row: Jan Pyk; Chris Reed; Frank Siteman;   3rd row: John Lei; Guadalupe de la Torre-Montano; Chris Demarest;   4th row: Lily Hong; John Lei; Kevin O'Malley

Table of Contents   4 Mary Lynn Blasutta;   6 Kevin O'Malley;   8 Chris Demarest

Illustration   10–13 Mary Lynn Blasutta;   14–26 Pat Cummings;   27 Fred Lynch;   28–29 (background) David White; Pat Cummings;   30–47 Aliki;   48–51 Guadaloupe de la Torre-Montano;   52–77 Jose Aruego and Ariane Dewey;

78–79 Mary Lynn Blasutta; **80–104** Cat Bowman Smith; **106–125** Paul Galdone; **127** Kevin O'Malley; **128–145** Veg Reisberg; **148** (top left), **150** (top left), **152** (top left) Cameron Gerlach; **148–149** Lily Hong; **150–151** Margaret Sanfilippo; **152–153** Cameron Gerlach; **154–155** Kevin O'Malley; **156–159** Chris Demarest; **160–185** Ivar Da Coll; **186** Luis Tomas; **187–189** Chris Reed; **190–210** Jennifer Northway; **211–215** Luis Tomas; **216–230** Akiko Hayaski; **231–235** Chris Demarest; **237–241** Leslie Wolf; **242, 243** (middle), **245, 247, 249, 251, 253, 256** (top) Jan Pyk; **243** (bottom), **248** Susan Miller; **243** (top), **244** (top), **250, 255, 256** (bottom) Lorretta Lustig; **244** (bottom), **252, 254** Rosiland Solomon; **257** Nancy Lee Walters

Photography **12** Courtesy of Alberto Barrera (bottom); **12** Ian Bradshaw (top right); **13** Michal Heron (right); **13** David Holter (left); **46** Alexa Brandenberg (middle); **47** Courtesy of Aliki Brandenberg (top); **51** Courtesy of Alberto Barrera; **74** David Holter; **75** Michal Heron; **76** A.T. Willett/The Image Bank (left); **76** Michal Heron (right); **77** C. Moore/The Image Bank (top); **77** Michal Heron (bottom); **105** Photo by Michael Ortiz, courtesy of Macmillan Publishing Company (top left); **105** Photo by Sue Smith, courtesy of Cat Bowman Smith (bottom right); **126** Photo by Suzanne Opton, courtesy of Clarion Books, a Houghton Mifflin Company; **146** Doug Thurston (center); **147** Dean Doerr (top); **147** Courtesy of Veg Reisberg (bottom); **232** Sergio Barbosa/Courtesy of Ivar Da Coll (top); **232** Courtesy Random Century Children's Books (bottom); **233** Norman Rubenis (top); **233** Fukuinkan Shoten Publishers, Inc. (center); **233** Fukuinkan Shoten Publishers, Inc. (bottom)

Assignment Photographers Ken Collins **12** (top), **28** (top); Dan Paul **236, 241**; Charles Seesselberg **28** (bottom), **29** (bottom)